A Maggie & Rose
Activity Book

This Book is Totally
Christmassy

Maggie, Rose, Oscar and Bentley totally love Christmas time.
They have oodles of fun festive ideas for stuff
to make and do, and they are looking forward
to sharing them with you and your family.

WALKER BOOKS
AND SUBSIDIARIES
LONDON · BOSTON · SYDNEY · AUCKLAND

Top-Secret Christmas Club Room

This is Maggie, Rose, Oscar and Bentley's secret club room and they have given it a super-special Christmas makeover.

Maggie loves decorating the tree.

Oscar loves all the tasty treats he can cook.

All activites in this book should be done with help from a grown-up.

Christmas is a great time for finding festive things to reuse and making fun stuff. Let's see what the gang got up to. But where is Bentley?

M & R

Rose loves making and wrapping presents.

Stringy Advent Calendar

Every home needs an advent calendar at Christmas. Instead of using chocolates, Maggie and Rose are showing Oscar how to make a "do something nice for someone" advent. Santa is watching so everyone is on their best behaviour!

STUFF TO USE

25 envelopes

Old Christmas wrapping paper and cards

Glitter

Sequins

Old cookie cutters

Felt-tip pens

Glue

25 pieces of card

String

Old Christmas ribbon

Hole punch

1. Decorate each envelope. Maggie is using glitter and old cookie cutters, Rose is drawing her own Christmas scenes and Oscar is using old wrapping paper to make a collage.

2. Think of some nice festive things to do and write them on the blank cards. Oscar has decided on "Sing Jingle Bells", "Give Daddy a hug" and "Leave a Christmassy surprise under Mummy's pillow". What will you choose?

3. Place one card in each envelope. Then mix them all up, so you don't know which card is in which envelope.

4. Number the back of each envelope with a date up to Christmas. (If it is the first day of December, number them 1–25.)

5. Hang the string on the wall like Christmassy bunting. Punch a hole in the corner of each envelope and tie them to the string with ribbon.

Take it in turns to open the envelopes — one every day until Christmas Day.

Decorating Day

On the first Sunday in December, Maggie's family invite friends over to decorate their Christmas tree. Everyone helps out and the kids make all sorts of stuff.

Gingerbread Dough

This is Maggie's scrummy recipe for Christmassy gingerbread dough. Try making it yourself!

STUFF TO USE

Bowl and spoon

350g plain flour

1-2 tsp ground ginger

1 tsp bicarbonate of soda

100g butter

175g soft light brown sugar

4 tbsps golden syrup

1 egg

Clingfilm

1. Mix the flour, ginger and soda together in a bowl and rub in the butter.

2. Add the sugar and stir in the syrup and the egg. Mix to make a firm dough.

3. Wrap the dough in clingfilm and keep in the fridge. Bring the dough back to room temperature before you want to use it.

Making Gingerbread Stars

To make these super-fabulous tasty decorations, follow Oscar.

1. Roll out the dough to about 2cm thick.

2. Using star-shaped cookie cutters, cut out a few stars. Oscar always makes extra so he can eat them!

3. Poke a hole in the top of each star with a straw.

4. Place the stars on a greased baking tray. Ask a grown-up to cook for 10–15 minutes at 180°C / 350°F / gas 4 until golden brown.

5. Once the stars have cooled down, decorate them using icing pens and silver balls. Then, thread raffia through the holes and tie in a loop.

6. Leave in the fridge to set for about 20 minutes.

STUFF TO USE

- Rolling pin
- Gingerbread dough
- Star-shaped cutters
- Straw
- Greased baking tray
- Icing pens
- Edible silver balls
- Raffia

Time to decorate the tree with stars!

Boxes for Stuff

Rose is making Maggie a special box so each year she can add a new decoration to it for the tree. It's useful for keeping other Christmassy things in too!

STUFF TO USE

Tin foil

Glue

Shoe box

Old Christmas cards

Scissors

1. Scrunch up the tin foil, then smooth it out again. This gives it a good texture.

2. Tear the tin foil into medium-sized squares.

3. Glue them onto your box, mosaic-style. Make sure you cover the lid as well.

4. Cut out letters from old Christmas cards to spell out the name you want. Stick them on the box.

5. Cut out fun festive pictures from the old cards. Stick them on the box too.

Make it look Christmassy!

Jolly Letters

Maggie is making a decoration of her own. It's very, very easy!

1. Roll out the red and green modelling clay into long strips.

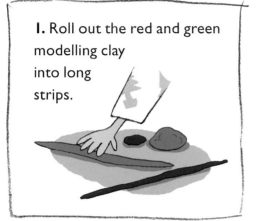

2. Take one strip of each colour and twist them together.

STUFF TO USE

Red and green modelling clay

Sequins

Pencil

Glue

Raffia

3. Shape the twist to make the first letter of your name. Add sequins to decorate.

4. Press the pencil through a top corner of the letter, making a hole.

Now it's ready to hang on the tree!

5. Paint your letter with glue and leave to dry overnight.

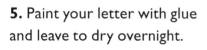

6. Thread the raffia through the hole and tie it in a loop.

Handmade Gifts

Maggie, Rose, Oscar and Bentley are experts at making their own presents. They are being super-secretive so others can't see what they are making. But if you promise not to tell, they will show you.

Christ_messy_ Paintings

Rose is making fun messy paintings for everyone, using lots of Christmassy colours. Oscar loves helping too.

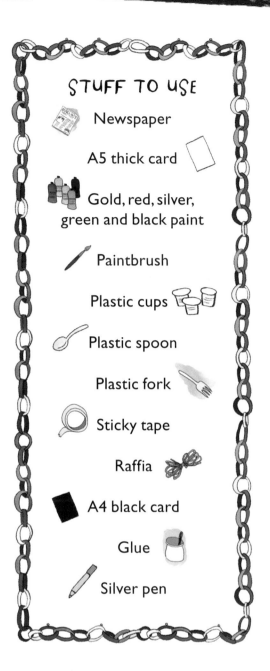

STUFF TO USE

- Newspaper
- A5 thick card
- Gold, red, silver, green and black paint
- Paintbrush
- Plastic cups
- Plastic spoon
- Plastic fork
- Sticky tape
- Raffia
- A4 black card
- Glue
- Silver pen

1. Cover your work area with lots of newspaper.

2. Paint the A5 card one colour all over – make sure it's a thick layer.

3. Mix the other paints with a tiny bit of water in plastic cups.

4. Artist Jackson Pollock dripped paint all over his canvas. Now it's your turn to do the same! Use a spoon and fork to dribble the paint over the card. Try dripping while standing up!

5. When you have finished your art, leave it flat to dry.

6. Use sticky tape to attach a loop of raffia to the back of the black card to make a hanging string.

7. Carefully mount your art onto the centre of the card frame with glue.

8. Make sure to sign the black card with the silver pen, so it will stand out.

All real artists sign their work — even Bentley!

STUFF TO USE

Bowl and spoon

Saucepan

Bar of chocolate

1 tbsp butter

2 cups crisped rice

1 cup dried cranberries

Greaseproof paper

Scissors

Sticky tape

Teaspoon

Baking tray

Icing sugar

Sieve

Clingfilm

Wishmas Trees

Rose is showing Maggie and Oscar how to make her Uncle Karl's famous Wishmas Trees. They are absolutely scrummy and bring you lots of luck with Christmas wishes.

1. Ask a grown-up to help you melt the chocolate. Break it into chunks, place in a bowl over a pot of simmering water and stir until it is completely melted.

2. Take off the heat. Add the butter and continue to stir.

3. Pour the crisped rice and cranberries into the melted chocolate. Mix well.

4. Cut the baking paper into four squares, roughly 20cm by 20cm. Roll each square into a cone shape and use sticky tape to hold in place.

5. Spoon the chocolate crispie mixture into the cones and press it down with your hands. Trim the base so it is flat.

6. Place face down on a baking tray and leave to set in the fridge for at least an hour.

7. When the chocolate has set, remove the paper.

8. Using a sieve, dust with icing sugar – as you do this, close your eyes and make a wish. But shhhh! Don't tell anyone or it won't come true!

Spread some Christmas wishes by wrapping Wishmas Trees in clingfilm and giving them to friends. Make a label that says, "make a wish on your Wishmas Tree!"

Merry Face Prints

Maggie is making a masterpiece to give to her granny for Christmas. Instead of a plain old photograph, she is making a piece of print art using her face! She is giving one to Rose, Oscar and Bentley as well — they will love it!

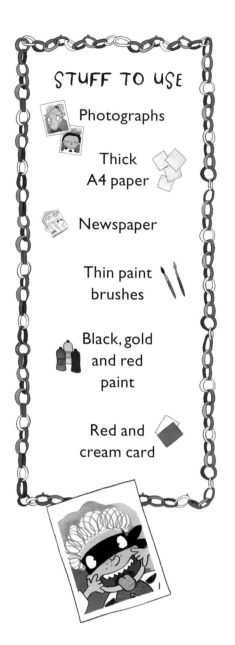
1. Choose some good photographs. Make sure they are a close-up of your face.

2. Ask a grown-up to print or photocopy at least ten photographs onto plain paper.

3. Cover your work area with newspaper. Paint over the outline of your face, eyes, mouth and some strands of hair. Make sure you paint thin lines and work quickly so the paint doesn't dry.

4. Carefully line up a piece of card and lay it on top. Press down with your hands.

5. Now comes the fun bit! Peel off the card and see what you have created.

6. You can paint over the photograph again using a different colour and print a second time to see what happens, or use another photograph and try again.

7. Keep experimenting until you get a couple of images that you are happy with. Don't forget to sign your print.

Maggie

Pop the pictures in a frame from the shops or make your own with colourful cardboard.

STUFF TO USE

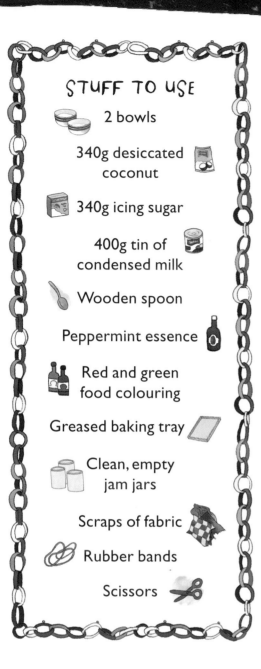

- 2 bowls
- 340g desiccated coconut
- 340g icing sugar
- 400g tin of condensed milk
- Wooden spoon
- Peppermint essence
- Red and green food colouring
- Greased baking tray
- Clean, empty jam jars
- Scraps of fabric
- Rubber bands
- Scissors

Icy Treats

Oscar is making extra-special Christmas coconut ice for everyone he knows. It's delicious! He has set up a festive factory — and you can too!

1. Mix the coconut and icing sugar together and then divide across two bowls, so there is half in each.

2. Add half the condensed milk to one bowl and stir very, very well with a wooden spoon. This is harder than it looks!

3. Add peppermint essence and green food colouring to the same bowl. Stir well.

4. Pour the green mix into a greased baking tray and flatten it with a wooden spoon. Leave to set for ten minutes.

5. In the second bowl, make up the mix in the same way but using red food colouring.

6. Carefully pour it on top of the green mixture and flatten it with a wooden spoon.

7. Leave to set for four to six hours. It's worth the wait!

8. Ask a grown-up to cut the ice into small squares. Take a peek at the coloured layers!

9. Place the squares into jam jars. Cut pieces of fabric big enough to cover the tops of the jars and fix with rubber bands.

Don't eat it all yourself!

Super Table Settings

Maggie and Rose love setting the table so they can make it look fabulous for Christmas dinner. They have invented pretty placemats and napkin rings that will make the table look very, very merry!

Pretty Placemats

1. Cut lengths of ribbon to cover the cake board, making sure each strip is long enough to go over the edges.

2. Cover the board in glue. This bit is messy but fun!

3. Stick strips of ribbon to the board in a criss-cross pattern.

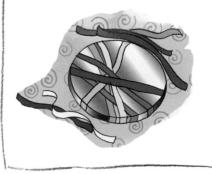

4. Once you have completely covered the board, leave to dry.

Everyone will want one!

Napkin Rings

1. Cut the toilet rolls into thick rings about 10cm wide. Make one ring per person.

2. Cover the rings in glue and wrap around strips of ribbon. Leave to dry.

3. Tie a Christmas decoration to each ring with raffia.

4. Put a rolled napkin through each ring and lay one next to every placemat.

STUFF TO USE

- Toilet roll tubes
- Scissors
- Glue
- Old Christmas ribbon
- Raffia
- Small Christmas decorations
- Napkins

Now it's time to set the table!

Santa works very, very hard on Christmas Eve delivering presents to all the children around the world. It's hungry business and he loves a little snack to keep him going. As Oscar is a super chef, he is baking Santa his favourite snacks — and he has invented a Santa Slurpie in case Santa is thirsty!

STUFF TO USE

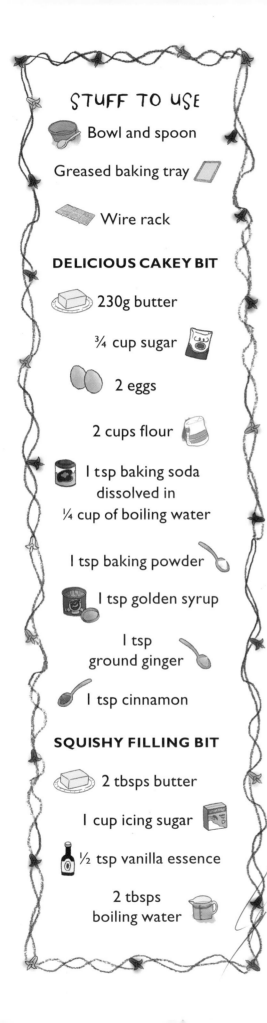

Bowl and spoon

Greased baking tray

Wire rack

DELICIOUS CAKEY BIT

230g butter

¾ cup sugar

2 eggs

2 cups flour

1 tsp baking soda dissolved in ¼ cup of boiling water

1 tsp baking powder

1 tsp golden syrup

1 tsp ground ginger

1 tsp cinnamon

SQUISHY FILLING BIT

2 tbsps butter

1 cup icing sugar

½ tsp vanilla essence

2 tbsps boiling water

Ginger Kisses

1. Cream together the butter and sugar in a bowl.

2. Add the eggs and mix together.

3. Add the rest of the "delicious cakey" ingredients. Stir very, very well (this is hard work!)

4. Put teaspoonfuls of batter on a cold, greased baking tray. Ask a grown-up to bake in a pre-heated oven at 160°C/325°F/gas 3 for 15 minutes.

5. When cooked, leave to cool on a wire cake rack.

6. Mix all the "squishy filling" ingredients together, beating until light and creamy.

7. Place a good dollop of the squishy filling onto a cakey bit, then grab another cakey bit and kiss them together like a sandwich.

make sure there are some left for Santa!

Santa Slurpie

STUFF TO USE

Bowl and spoon

Saucepan

½ bar peppermint chocolate

1 cup warm milk

2 tbsps double cream

Glass

White mini marshmallows

1. Ask a grown-up to melt the chocolate in a bowl over a pot of simmering water.

2. Take the chocolate off the heat and slowly stir in the warm milk.

3. Stir in the double cream.

4. Pour into a tall glass and sprinkle with marshmallows.

Leave out for Santa to slurp up after his Ginger kisses!

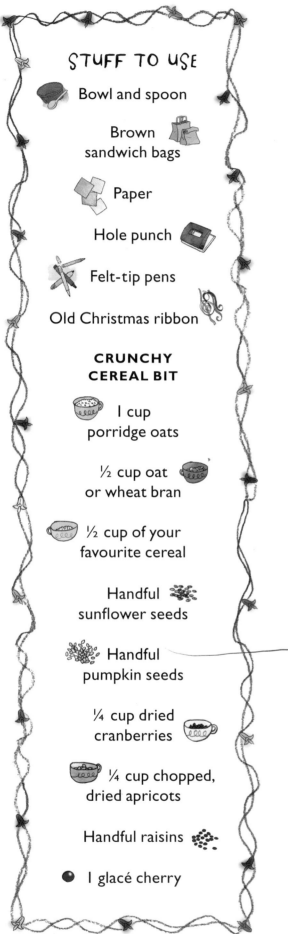

STUFF TO USE

- Bowl and spoon
- Brown sandwich bags
- Paper
- Hole punch
- Felt-tip pens
- Old Christmas ribbon

CRUNCHY CEREAL BIT

- 1 cup porridge oats
- ½ cup oat or wheat bran
- ½ cup of your favourite cereal
- Handful sunflower seeds
- Handful pumpkin seeds
- ¼ cup dried cranberries
- ¼ cup chopped, dried apricots
- Handful raisins
- 1 glacé cherry

Reindeer Snacks

When Oscar grows up he wants to be the head elf in charge of reindeer in Santa's workshop! He has invented some super snacks to give them energy to help Santa deliver all the presents on Christmas Eve.

Red Nose Cereal

1. Combine the three cereals in a big bowl, giving the mixture a good toss with your hands.

2. Add the sunflower and pumpkin seeds.

3. Add the dried fruit and toss again.

4. Add the cherry – also known as Rudolph's nose. This is the surprise ingredient! Who will get it?

5. Place a big spoonful in nine sandwich bags. Be careful not to spill any!

6. Tear small pieces of paper, punch a hole in the corners and label each with a reindeer's name. Tie to the bags with ribbon.

7. Leave the bags on a table with a jug of milk and some honey (this is how reindeer like to eat their snacks).

8. If the reindeer have left any behind on Christmas morning, you can eat it for energy before you open your presents. Mmmmm, delicious!

Do you know all the names of Santa's reindeer? Which reindeer has Bentley replaced?

Answers: Dasher, Dancer, Prancer, Vixen, Comet, Cupid, Donner, Blitzen, Rudolph (or should that be Bentley!)

Santa's Footsteps

This is a fun and easy way to make sure that Santa finds your stocking on Christmas Eve! Oscar is making a top-secret trail for Santa to follow.

STUFF TO USE

Old Christmas wrapping paper

Cardboard

Glue

Pen

Scissors

1. Work out how Santa will come into your house – through the chimney, window, or door?

2. Count the steps from there to your stocking.

3. Glue the wrapping paper to the cardboard.

4. On the other side of the card, draw around your feet lots of times. Cut out the foot shapes.

5. Draw and cut out some arrows too.

6. Use the feet and arrows to lay out a trail, from start to finish.

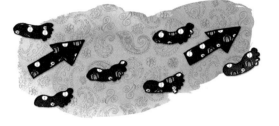

Now Santa won't get lost!

Present Swap Game

The day after Christmas can be a little dull as you have opened all the presents. Play this silly swapping game and you can reuse leftover presents and old wrapping paper — it's loads of fun!

Stuff to Find and Prepare

STUFF TO USE

Old Christmas wrapping paper

Sticky tape

Scissors

A4 card

Pen

Blowers, whistles and bells

1. Let the present hunt begin! Ask the grown-ups for any leftover Christmassy things that can be used as presents. Each player needs three — two silly and one extra special treat. You could use some of the lovely stuff you have made.

2. Use old wrapping paper and sticky tape to wrap the presents up in secret. Then get everyone to place the presents in a pile.

3. Cut the cards into squares and write oodles of fun Christmassy questions on the back. You might want to write something like Maggie, or look up fun facts on your computer.

Can you sing the next two lines? "We wish you a merry Christmas..."

How to Play the Game

1. Take it in turns to ask the questions. Players must use their buzzer to answer – a buzzer can be anything that makes noise, like a whistle or a bell.

2. Every correct answer means you get to pick a present from the pile – but don't open it yet!

3. Once all the presents have been won, swap a present with someone else every time you get an answer correct. Play for as long as you like.

4. Open your presents! You may need to swap presents back – who wants dad's socks?

Who will win the most presents?

Festive Fun Scrapbook

Maggie and Rose are making a super scrapbook of Christmas memories. It's a great project for the whole family over the Christmas holidays!

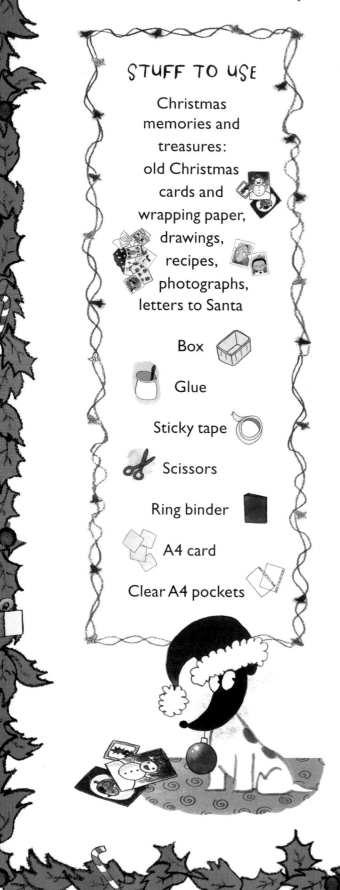

1. Get all the family to gather as many Christmas memories and treasures as they can. Keep them in a box.

2. Gather around a big table with the ring binder and get glue, sticky tape and scissors for everyone. Don't forget your special memory box!

3. Decorate the front of the ring binder using old wrapping paper and whatever else you fancy.

4. Give everyone pieces of card and get them to write down or glue on the Christmassy memories and treasures that they have collected.

5. Put each completed page in a clear pocket to keep it safe.

Take your scrapbook out each Christmas and see what you did the year before!

6. Create sections to put everything in. Rose has labelled hers "What We Ate," "Photos from Christmases Past," "My First Christmas," and "Decorations." What will your sections be?

Christmassy Thank Yous

It is most important to say a proper thank you for all the lovely gifts you receive.
Using all the leftover wrapping paper and cards from Christmas Day it's super-easy to make little thank you trinkets.

Cheery Postcards

STUFF TO USE

- Old Christmas cards
- Scissors
- Old Christmas wrapping paper
- Glue
- Writing paper
- Felt-tip pens
- Pencil

1. Cut some Christmas cards in half.

2. Glue scraps of wrapping paper to cover both sides of one half of card.

3. Tear two pieces of writing paper to fit the middle of the front and back sides.
Glue them on.
Be sure to leave a border of wrapping paper.

4. On the front, in your bestest handwriting write "Thank You" using felt-tip pens.

5. On the back, draw a line down the middle of the paper. Write your thank you note on the left-hand side.

6. Write the address on the right-hand side.

Pop on a stamp, ready to post.

Happy Wall Hanging

I. Measure the ribbon to all four edges of the card and cut to size to make a frame.

2. Glue the frame to the card.

STUFF TO USE

- ☐ Thick A4 card
- Christmas ribbon
- Glue
- Raffia
- Sticky tape
- Felt-tip pens

3. Sticky tape the raffia to the back of the card in a loop, so it will hang.

4. Write a thank you on the front — you can just spell out "Thank you," write your own thank you poem, or copy Oscar's poem. Sign it with lots of Christmassy kisses.

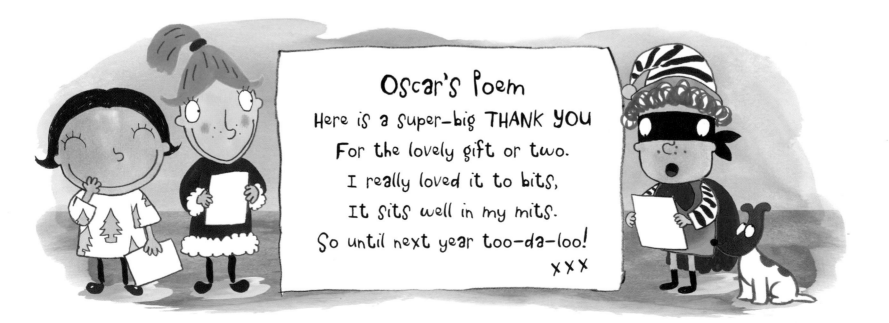

Oscar's Poem

Here is a super-big THANK YOU
For the lovely gift or two.
I really loved it to bits,
It sits well in my mits.
So until next year too-da-loo!
XXX

Did You Know?

Christmas trees are edible. The needles on pines, spruces and firs contain lots of vitamin C like an orange – but don't try eating them straight off the tree!

What other fun facts can you find out? Use your computer to look some up.

Reindeers are good at pulling Santa's sleigh, but they are also really good swimmers.

If you received all of the gifts in the song "The Twelve Days of Christmas", you would have 364 gifts.